Stories For

year-olds

Contents

This edition published in 2022 by
Baker and Taylor (UK) Ltd,
Bicester, Oxfordshire OX26 4ST

Curious Universe UK Ltd
UK - The Ice House, 124-126 Walcot Street, Bath BA1 5BG
EU - Suite 106, 3 Lombard St East, Dublin 2
www.curiousuniverse.co.uk

© Hinkler Pty Ltd 2021
All rights reserved.

Story author: Vanessa Battersby
Story illustrator: Belinda Strong
Nursery rhymes illustrations: Shutterstock.com
Design: Aimee Zumis

ISBN: 978 1 8651 5427 5

CUL2004

Printed and bound in China

Stories for

year-olds

Welcome to
Stories for 1-year-olds

Storytime can be the snuggliest part of the day with
your 1-year-old – reading together, enjoying the pictures and bright colours,
and perhaps having fun acting out nursery rhymes!

Reading aloud is also one of the best things you can do for your baby. Did you
know that the most dramatic language development occurs between the
ages of one and two? At one, most children are still babbling; at two, they
can use up to 50 words and say simple phrases. Research shows that you can
actively increase a baby's vocabulary if you read to them every day, so this is
the perfect time to begin a regular storytime routine!

Stories for 1-year-olds contains four sweet, simple stories to enjoy
with your child, especially written to be accessible and engaging
for 1-year-olds. Words are kept to a minimum and illustrations
are kept engaging and bright!

These four stories are
interspersed with over 20 fun nursery
rhymes and lullabies, as rhyming helps babies
develop language skills by showcasing different sounds
in a rhythmic and interactive way that you can use to
bond with your little one.

Morning Time follows a child through their morning, including eating
breakfast, getting dressed – and, of course, cuddles!

In *Playtime*, we play with toys at home, have a friend visit, and go to the park
for fresh air and giggles. Clapping and peekaboo make playtime fun – and
the nursery rhymes that follow pick up on the theme, including classics
like 'Pat-a-cake' and 'Ten Little Fingers'.

After playtime comes *Naptime*! Tuck your child in with their comfy pillow, a blanket
and a kiss, and wake them up later with some entertaining nursery rhymes!

When the day draws to a close, it's *Bedtime*. Your little one will love following
along with the pictures of bath time, teeth-brushing and storytime!
Finish with calming rhymes and lullabies to soothe your baby to sleep.

Happy reading!

Morning Time

Look at the **sunshine**!
What a happy day!

Good morning, everyone!

I **stretch** with Mummy.

Pick me **up** please!

Daddy gives me lots of **cuddles**.

I eat **breakfast** and fill my tummy.

It's **yummy**!

Milk is delicious!

Mummy puts my **shoes** on – we're going out! Hooray!

Baa, Baa, Black Sheep

Baa, baa, black sheep,
Have you any wool?
Yes, sir, yes, sir,
Three bags full.

One for the master,
And one for the dame,
And one for the little boy
who lives down
the lane.

Hey, Diddle, Diddle

Hey, diddle, diddle!
The cat and the fiddle,
The cow jumped over the moon;
The little dog laughed
To see such sport,
And the dish ran away with the spoon.

Chook, Chook, Chook-chook-chook

Chook, chook, chook-chook-chook,
Good morning Mrs Hen,
How many chickens have you got?
Madam, I've got ten.

Four of them are yellow,
And four of them are brown,
And two of them are speckled red,
The nicest in the town.

Row, Row, Row Your Boat

Row, row, row your boat,
Gently down the stream.
Merrily, merrily, merrily, merrily,
Life is but a dream.

The Muffin Man

Oh, do you know the muffin man,
The muffin man, the muffin man,
Do you know the muffin man,
Who lives in Drury Lane?

Oh yes, I know the muffin man,
The muffin man, the muffin man,
Yes, I know the muffin man,
Who lives in Drury Lane.

Incy Wincy Spider

Incy Wincy Spider
climbed up the water spout,
Down came the rain
and washed poor Incy out.

Out came the sunshine
and dried up all the rain,
And Incy Wincy Spider
climbed up the spout again!

Playtime

It's playtime!
I like to shake my **rattle**.

My **train** carries lots of toys.
Choo-choo!

A **friend** has come to play!
Hello!

'Let's all go to the **park**!'
Mummy says.

Mummy pushes me on the **swing**. Whee!

My friend calls, 'Look, I'm on
the **slide**!'

We **clap**. 'You slid so fast!'

Now let's play. 'Peekaboo!'

Playtime means **giggles**!

Pat-a-cake

Pat-a-cake, pat-a-cake, baker's man.
Bake me a cake as fast as you can;
Pat it and prick it and mark it with B,
Put it in the oven for baby and me.

Ten Little Fingers

I have ten little fingers,
And they all belong to me.
I can make them do things,
Would you like to see?

I can shut them up tight,
Or open them wide.
I can put them together,
Or make them all hide.

I can make them jump high,
I can make them go low.
I can fold them up quietly,
And hold them just so.

This Little Piggy

This little piggy went to market,
This little piggy stayed at home;
This little piggy had roast beef,
This little piggy had none;
And this little piggy cried, 'Wee-wee-wee!'
All the way home.

Market

43

Here is the Beehive

Here is the beehive,
But where are the bees?
Hidden away,
Where nobody sees.
Watch and you'll see them
Come out of the hive.
One, two, three, four, five.
Bzzzzzzzz!

Old MacDonald Had a Farm

Old MacDonald had a farm, E-I-E-I-O!
And on that farm he had a cow, E-I-E-I-O!
With a moo moo here and a moo moo there,
Here a moo, there a moo,
Everywhere a moo moo!
Old MacDonald had a farm, E-I-E-I-O!

Old MacDonald had a farm, E-I-E-I-O!
And on that farm he had a pig, E-I-E-I-O!
With an oink oink here and an oink oink there...

Old MacDonald had a farm, E-I-E-I-O!
And on that farm he had a horse, E-I-E-I-O!
With a neigh neigh here and a neigh neigh there...

Old MacDonald had a farm, E-I-E-I-O!
And on that farm he had a duck, E-I-E-I-O!
With a quack quack here and a quack quack there...

Old MacDonald had a farm, E-I-E-I-O!
And on that farm he had a dog, E-I-E-I-O!
With a woof woof here and a woof woof there...

I'm a Little Teapot

I'm a little teapot, short and stout,
Here is my handle, here is my spout.
When I get all steamed up, hear me shout,
Tip me over and pour me out!

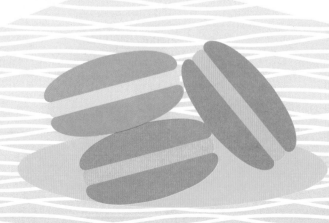

One Elephant Went Out to Play

One elephant went out to play,
Upon a spider's web one day.
He had such enormous fun,
That he called for another elephant to come.

Two elephants went out to play,
Upon a spider's web one day.
They had such enormous fun,
That they called for another elephant to come.

Three elephants went out to play...

Four elephants went out to play...

Five elephants went out to play,
Upon a spider's web one day.
The web went creak, the web went crack,
And five elephants came running back!

Naptime

I'm so **sleepy**.

Daddy **hugs** me. 'It's time for a nap!' he says.

'Here's your nice soft **pillow**.'
Daddy gives it to me.

My **blanket** is so warm and cosy.

I **love** naptime!

Daddy tucks me in. 'Snuggle up!'

'Daddy, please sing me a **lullaby**?'
He smiles and sings.

'Here's a **kiss**, moppet.
Sleep well.'

'Sweet dreams!'

Once I Saw a Little Bird

Once I saw a little bird
come hop, hop, hop;
So I cried, 'Little bird
will you stop, stop, stop?'
I was going to the window,
To say 'How do you do?'
But he shook his little tail,
And far away he flew.

Polly Put the Kettle On

Polly put the kettle on,
Polly put the kettle on,
Polly put the kettle on,
We'll all have tea.

Sukey take it off again,
Sukey take it off again,
Sukey take it off again,
They've all gone away.

Three Blind Mice

Three blind mice, three blind mice.
See how they run! See how they run!
They all ran after the farmer's wife,
Who cut off their tails with a carving knife;
Did you ever see such a sight in your life,
As three blind mice?

Five Little Monkeys

Five little monkeys,
jumping on the bed;
One fell off
And bumped his head.
Mama called the doctor,
The doctor said:
'No more monkeys
Jumping on the bed!'

Four little monkeys,
Jumping on the bed...

Three little monkeys,
Jumping on the bed...

Two little monkeys,
Jumping on the bed...

One little monkey,
Jumping on the bed...

One, Two, Three, Four, Five

One, two, three, four, five,
Once I caught a fish alive;
Six, seven, eight, nine, ten,
Then I let it go again.

Why did you let it go?
Because it bit my finger so.
Which finger did it bite?
This little finger on the right.

Bingo

There was a farmer had a dog,
And Bingo was his name-o.
B-I-N-G-O!
B-I-N-G-O!
B-I-N-G-O!
And Bingo was his name-o!

There was a farmer had a dog...
(clap)-I-N-G-O! (x 3)
And Bingo was his name-o!

There was a farmer had a dog...
(clap)-(clap)-N-G-O! (x 3)
And Bingo was his name-o!

There was a farmer had a dog...
(clap)-(clap)-(clap)-G-O! (x 3)
And Bingo was his name-o!

There was a farmer had a dog...
(clap)-(clap)-(clap)-(clap)-O! (x 3)
And Bingo was his name-o!

There was a farmer had a dog...
(clap)-(clap)-(clap)-(clap)-(clap)! (x 3)
And Bingo was his name-o!

Two Little Black Birds

Two little black birds,
Sitting on a wall;

One named Peter,
One named Paul.

Fly away Peter!
Fly away Paul!

Come back Peter!
Come back Paul!

Mary Had a Little Lamb

Mary had a little lamb,
its fleece was white as snow.
And everywhere that Mary went,
the lamb was sure to go.

It followed her to school one day
which was against the rule.
It made the children laugh and play,
to see a lamb at school!

And so the teacher turned it out,
but still it lingered near,
and waited patiently about,
till Mary did appear.

'What makes the lamb love Mary so?'
the eager children cry.
'Why, Mary loves the lamb, you know.'
the teacher did reply.

Bedtime

The moon says, 'It's **bath time**!'
And so it is. Splish, splash!

Where's my **toothbrush**?
Scrub-a-scrub – all nice and fresh.

I'm **tired** now. Yawn!

The **stars** peep in quietly – see them twinkle?

'Is it **storytime** yet?'

Teddy tells us a lovely story.

He's very nice to **cuddle**, too!

Every night, I see the **moon**.
Hello, moon!

Goodnight, everyone!

Twinkle, Twinkle, Little Star

Twinkle, twinkle, little star,
How I wonder what you are.
Up above the world so high,

Like a diamond in the sky.
Twinkle, twinkle, little star,
How I wonder what you are!

All the Pretty Little Horses

Hush-a-bye, don't you cry,
Go to sleep, little baby.
When you wake
You shall have
All the pretty little horses,
Black and bays, dapples and greys,
Coach and six white horses.

Hush-a-bye, don't you cry,
Go to sleep, little baby.
When you wake
You shall have cake
And all the pretty little horses.

Rock-a-bye Baby

Rock-a-bye baby, on the treetop,
When the wind blows, the cradle will rock;
When the bough breaks, the cradle will fall,
Down will come baby, cradle and all.

Brahms' Lullaby

Lullaby and goodnight,
With roses bestride,
With lillies bedecked,
'Neath baby's sweet bed.

May thou sleep, may thou rest,
May thy slumber be blest,
May thou sleep, may thou rest,
May thy slumber be blest.

Lullaby and goodnight,
Thy mothers's delight.
Bright angels around
My darling shall guard.

They will guide thee from harm,
Thou art safe in my arms.
They will guide thee from harm,
Thou art safe in my arms.

Sweet Dreams!

Goodnight!